MORE FUN WITH FIGURES

by

PHILIP E. BATH

compiler of
Fun With Words
Fun With Figures
Fun With Words Again
A Biblical Quiz
How Much Do *You* Know?

LONDON
THE EPWORTH PRESS

PRINTED IN GREAT BRITAIN BY
THE SIDNEY PRESS LTD., BEDFORD

NOTE

More Fun With Figures follows the pattern of the author's previous volume of figure puzzles. The solution of many of the problems, especially the earlier ones, is well within the range of the intelligent young teenager; none requires any deep knowledge of mathematics. An understanding of simple arithmetical processes, an ability to think clearly and a mind always on the alert for the carefully baited trap—these are the only assets required of the solver.

In order that any difficulties shall be cleared up, the author has, in most cases, supplemented the answers with an explanation how they may be obtained.

It is hoped that this selection of puzzles will not only provide further entertainment for those already figure-minded, but also help to persuade others that playing with figures can be very good fun and, at the same time, a pleasant means of picking up some useful and interesting information on the way.   P.E.B.

1. THE QUARREL

Jack and Jill were standing in a field 20 yards apart, Jack facing north and Jill facing south. It would seem that they had quarrelled. After a time, however, Jack walked slowly 4 yards forward, to which Jill replied by walking 3 yards backward. How far were they apart now?

2. FIND THE TRAIL

Beginning at 1, and moving only horizontally or vertically, you are required to trace a course from square 1 to square 49 by writing in the missing numbers in such a way that your trail is one of a series of consecutive numbers. Naturally no square may be passed through twice.

		19				
		4				
			23			
14	9		1			30
						36
49		42				

3. SQUARE AND RECTANGLE

Draw a square on a piece of paper. Now can you with two cuts obtain a number of pieces which can be fitted together to form a rectangle twice as long as it is wide?

5

4. PETE'S PUZZLE

'How many pennies have you in your pocket, Pete?'

'I'll tell you. When I have multiplied what I've got by the number of pennies I've got, I shall have the same amount as I shall have when I've added as much as I've got to what I've got now.'

Pete's pal was really puzzled. Are you?

5. BLOTS!

144 square pieces of wood each of 4 square feet can be cut from a piece of wood measuring 8 ▓▓▓▓▓

This was the answer—and a correct one—to a sum which had been worked by Master Charlie Careless, who excelled in making blots all over his book. Now, what words were concealed beneath this particular blot?

6. TWO SQUARES OF SQUARES

Can you replace the asterisks by figures so that the 4 numbers in each square when read clockwise are all perfect squares? Moreover, it is required that all 8 numbers shall be different.

```
*   *   *     *   *   *

*       *   *       *

*   *   *     *   *   *
```

7. THE MAZE

Jack, after reaching the centre of a maze, set out on the return journey. The pattern of the maze is shown by the diagram opposite, the figures indicating the number of paces along each straight stretch. Jack finally emerged into the open after he had walked two successive stretches of 100 paces, each in a different direction. How many paces had he taken altogether on his return journey?

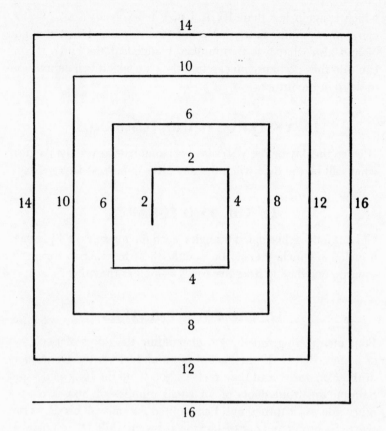

8. ANAGRAMS

E = 9   I = 1   M = 6   T = 2

The four letters above can be used to form a number of different words. Can you say what is the word whose letter values when written down in order will give a number which is a perfect square?

9. NUMBER MAGIC

I think of a number less than 10. I multiply this by 5 and then add 3. Next I multiply my answer by 2 and then add any number which is again less than 10. If I now tell you my final answer, can you say immediately what was the number I first thought of and also what was the number I added at the end? If you can't do this, perhaps you can find the clue which will enable you to do so in the future.

10. YESTERDAY AND TOMORROW

If when the day before yesterday was tomorrow it was 1st August, what will be the date when the day after tomorrow is yesterday?

11. THE TWO SQUARES

Cut out four right-angled triangles, each having sides of $4\frac{1}{2}$ inches, 6 inches, $7\frac{1}{2}$ inches. Can you now fit these together to form two squares, one having sides five times as long as the other?

12. THE FOUR PAINTERS

Four men were given the job of painting the doors of two rows of houses, Bell to do the back doors and Jackson the front doors of those on one side of the street, Dalton to do the back doors and Samson the front doors of an equal number of houses on the other side. As it turned out, Bell painted not only all his doors but two of Samson's and one of Jackson's as well, while Dalton painted four of Jackson's doors and two of Samson's in addition to his own. How many more doors did each of the other three paint than the one who did the least?

13. NAMES WANTED

Can you put a name to each of the following, some of which are approximations?

(a) $\frac{5}{8}$ mile
(b) $1\frac{1}{11}$ yards
(c) $1\frac{3}{4}$ pints
(d) $2\frac{1}{5}$ lb
(e) $37\frac{1}{2}$ gallons (of herrings)
(f) $\frac{2}{5}$ inch
(g) 6,080 feet per hour
(h) 4 inches
(i) 32 feet per second per second
(j) -273 degrees Centigrade

8

14. MORNING EXERCISE

My house is exactly half-way along the bus route from Northwick bus station to Southwick bus station. Buses cover the 8 miles between them in 20 minutes. Each morning I leave my house to go to my office at the bus station at Southwick and, being keen on a certain amount of daily exercise, I walk to the Mason's Arms, which is half-way between my house and my office. By walking at a steady 3 miles an hour I can be sure of arriving at the Mason's Arms just in time to board the bus leaving Northwick at 8.25 a.m. At what time do I leave home each morning?

15. AN INFREQUENT OCCURRENCE

The figures of the year 1961 read the same upside down. How many times has this happened previously since, and including, the year 1 A.D.? Also how many years will elapse before this happens again?

16. WIRE-CUTTING

Given a piece of stout wire 12 inches long, what is the least number of cuts you must make so that you have sufficient pieces of wire to make four equilateral triangles?

17. A PERMANENT CALENDAR

You are given a number of pieces of cardboard of the following dimensions, 1 in. × 1¼ in., 1½ in. × 1¼ in., 2 in. × 1¼ in., with which to make one of those permanent calendars. This you will do by writing on the smallest cards the day numbers, on the middle size the names of the months, and on the largest the names of the days. When this is done the cards will be fitted into a suitable holder so that the cards can be changed to show the days and dates throughout any year. What is the minimum number of cards of each size you will require for this purpose?

18. DOMINOES

Without actually counting them, can you say how many spots there are on a set of dominoes?

19. UNUSUAL DATES

14th November 1411 can be written as 14.11.1411, in which case the day number with the month number written alongside it is the same as the number of the year. When was the last time that there was a similar occurrence and when will it happen next?

20. QUITE A FAMILY

There are 8 children in the Johnson family. The first four were born at intervals of 2 years, after which there was a gap of $6\frac{1}{2}$ years. Then came the remaining four at intervals of $2\frac{1}{2}$ years. On her last birthday Gillian, the eldest, was just 6 times as old as Barbara, the youngest. What was Gillian's age then?

21. A DISSECTION PROBLEM

Can you cut a piece of paper like that represented below into 8 pieces, all of which can be placed on top of one another so that the edges coincide exactly?

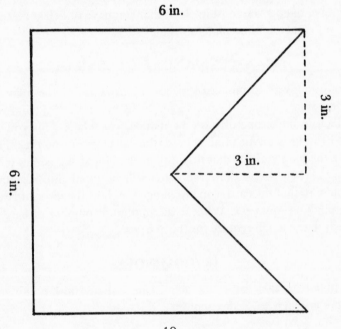

6 in.

6 in.

3 in.

3 in.

22. AN ENGLISH LITERARY GENIUS

A person with an eye for figures can often remember a particular combination of digits by some special peculiarity which they exhibit. Take, for instance, the years of the birth and death of one of England's great literary geniuses. The square root of the number formed by the first two digits of the year of his death, and the square root of the number formed by the last two digits of the year of his death, and the square root of the sum of the digits of the year of his birth are all the same whole number, which is just half the square root of the number formed by the last two digits of the year of his birth. From which it should not be difficult to determine the dates in question.

23. SUMMER TIME AND REAL TIME

What time, according to the clock, is sunset in London on 26th August if on that day midnight real time is as many hours after sunset British Summer Time as midnight real time is before 6 a.m. British Summer Time next day?

24. A DIFFERENT SORT OF MAGIC SQUARE

In the square below, can you replace the letters by figures so that all the 5 rows of numbers, no matter whether they are read backwards or forwards; all the 5 columns of numbers, no matter whether they are read up or down; and the numbers formed by the 2 diagonals, whichever way they are read, are in every case exactly divisible by 4? A different letter represents, of course, a different number. There are two possible solutions.

A	b	b	b	A
b	A	b	A	b
b	b	A	b	b
b	A	b	A	b
A	b	b	b	A

25. WHO'S FIRST?

This problem has many solutions, but go into competition with your friends to see who can produce one correct solution first. The problem is to replace the asterisks by any of the numbers 1–24 (other than 1, 7, 9, 10, 17, 23, which have already been used) so that the six statements read true. No number must be used more than once throughout.

$$1 + * + * + * = 50$$

$$7 + * + * + * = 50$$

$$9 + * + * + * = 50$$

$$10 + * + * + * = 50$$

$$17 + * + * + * = 50$$

$$23 + * + * + * = 50$$

26. THE CHILDREN'S MONEY-BOXES

When the four children emptied their money-boxes, which were found to contain 10 shillings in all, I was struck by the fact that if one wrote down the four different amounts, each a prime number of pennies, one would need to use only two different digits. This suggested to me that it might be an interesting puzzle for others to try to discover how much there was in each of the boxes.

27. WASTE NOT, WANT NOT

If to be economical is a virtue, then Mr Smith was certainly virtuous. Each Saturday he bought his week's supply of cigarettes, but each week he always enjoyed more cigarettes than the number he bought. This he achieved by saving all the ends of all the cigarettes he smoked and making out of every 10 ends one more cigarette. The total cigarettes he smoked in any one week was 111, with 1 end left over to add to his future accumulation of ends. How many cigarettes would you say Mr Smith bought each Saturday?

28. ARE YOU SURE?

How many different squares and how many different rectangles which are not squares can you count in the 9-cell square below?

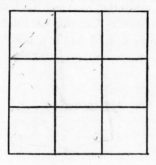

29. A NUMERICAL TABLE

Here are the first nine lines of one of the ordinary numerical tables. Each letter stands for the same figure throughout. The lines of the table as here given do not, however, run consecutively. Can you by a little simple deduction reproduce the table in its usual numerical form?

A × K = EF   F × K = DH

B × K = K   G × K = EB

C × K = HG   H × K = AE

D × K = GD   K × K = AC

E × K = BA

30. BROTHERS AND SISTERS

In a certain family each brother had as many sisters as he had brothers and each of the sisters had three times as many brothers as she had sisters. How many boys and how many girls were there in the family?

13

31. QUICK WORK

Here is an addition sum of 7 items of which 3 items are missing. You will notice that each of the given items contains all the digits from 1–8. Can you fill in the 3 missing lines, each line again containing all the digits from 1–8, so that the total as given is correct? Does it surprise you to be told that it is possible to do this in less than 30 seconds?

$$
\begin{array}{cccccccc}
1 & 2 & 3 & 4 & 5 & 6 & 7 & 8 \\
* & * & * & * & * & * & * & * \\
2 & 3 & 4 & 5 & 6 & 7 & 8 & 1 \\
5 & 6 & 7 & 8 & 1 & 2 & 3 & 4 \\
* & * & * & * & * & * & * & * \\
3 & 4 & 5 & 6 & 7 & 8 & 1 & 2 \\
* & * & * & * & * & * & * & *
\end{array}
$$

$$
3\ 5\ 6\ 7\ 8\ 1\ 2\ 3\ 1
$$

32. A RAILWAY CONTRACT

A city has 5 railway termini, from each of which it is decided to run 3 separate railway tracks to 3 different docks. The contract for the building of these lines stipulated that there were to be no tunnels or bridges and no intersection of lines. How many of the city's stations had been connected to the 3 docks when the contractor was compelled to inform the railway authority that the contract would have to be altered if the work was to be completed?

14

33. WHAT IS THE SERIES?

The asterisks below represent numbers, obtained by multiplying various sets of two numbers whose total is in every case the same. The series, of which this is only a part, is one which rises to a maximum of 144, after which it declines. Can you reproduce the complete series?

*   *   *   *   144   *   *   *   *

34. DARTS

The number of points which a dart player can score at one throw is any single number from 1–20, a 'double' of any of these numbers, a 'treble' of any of these numbers, 25, or 50. What, then, is the minimum number of throws required to score 1,001 and how would this score be obtained?

35. CAR MILEAGE

When I recorded my car mileage last week I found it to be exactly double that of the week before, making a total of between 800 and 900 miles for the two weeks. This two-week total was most unusual in one respect, for in writing down those two mileages and their total I used every one of the digits from 1–9. Can you deduce what was my mileage in each of the two weeks in question?

36. A DIVIDED FARM

A farmer owned a piece of land 400 yards square which was enclosed by a fence. On his retirement this was divided among his 5 sons as follows : The eldest son had a quarter, also square in shape, and to which he had access without crossing any of his brothers' plots. The rest was divided equally among the other 4 sons so that each man's plot, although not square in this case, was exactly the same shape as that of each of the other three. How many yards of additional fencing had to be bought in order to enclose the 5 plots?

37. VERY MUCH A SKELETON

Here is a very much skeletonized multiplication sum in which all the figures in any one vertical column of the six partial products are the same. Can you reproduce the complete sum with its answer?

```
                    *  *  *  *  *  *
                 ×  *  *  *  *  *  *
                 ──────────────────
                    *  *  *  *  *  *
                 *  *  *  *  *  *
              *  *  *  *  *  *
           *  *  *  *  *  *
        *  *  *  *  *  *
     *  *  *  *  *  *
  ─────────────────────────────────
  4  2  8  5  7  1
  ─────────────────────────────────
  *  *  *  *  *  *  *  *  *  *  *  *
  ═════════════════════════════════
```

38. THE ROSE-GARDEN

```
              *

           *  *  *

        *  *  *  *  *

     *  *  *  *  *  *  *
```

The above shows the pattern of the layout of a nurseryman's rose-garden. In actual fact there were 59 rose-trees along the base of the triangle, with other trees arranged in columns and rows as above; that is, the row immediately previous to the base

16

had 57 trees, the one previous to that had 55 trees, and so on. If each tree cost 5 shillings, how much money had the nurseryman expended on his plot?

39. THE BIRTHDAY PARTY

At a birthday party were 4 brothers and 4 sisters whose combined ages were 62 years. Bertha was 3 years old, Gillian was 4 years old, Pat was 5 years old, and Ruth was 7 years old. The 4 brothers were George Collins, who was a twin to his sister; Richard Dawson, who was twice as old as his sister; George Adams, who was 3 times as old as his sister; Freddie Brown, who was 4 times as old as his sister. Can you give the correct surname of each girl?

40. THE MISSING SHOES

It would have saved a lot of trouble if every boy at the school had replaced his gym shoes in his own locker after use. Instead, the lazy ones would throw theirs in a corner of the cloak-room, with the inevitable result that when the next lesson was due some were missing. On one such occasion the upshot was this: 4 boys had no left-foot shoes, 3 had no right-foot shoes, 4 had right-foot shoes and 3 had left-foot shoes. What was the minimum number of boys who must have found themselves without a pair of shoes?

41. THE SILVER WEDDING

At a silver wedding party there were present: 1 grandfather, 1 grandmother, 2 fathers, 2 mothers, 1 father-in-law, 1 mother-in-law, 4 sons, 1 daughter, 3 daughters-in-law, 3 brothers, 1 sister, 1 grandson, 3 sisters-in-law, 2 uncles, 3 aunts, 1 nephew. A large party you will say. No, not as large as you may think, since the company was the smallest which would provide all these relationships. How many, then, would you say made up the party?

42. A CURRENCY CHANGE

On 1st January 1961 the farthing ceased to be legal tender. To what extent did this affect the number of possible ways in which one can give change for a sixpence?

43. THREE ADDITIONS

You are asked to replace the asterisks in the 3 addition sums by figures in such a way that (a) in each case the 3 items to be added consist of all the digits from 1–9; (b) in each case the second of these items is double the first and the third is three times the first; (c) the difference between the totals of the first and second is the same as that between the totals of the second and third.

```
  *  *  *        *  *  *        *  *  *

  *  *  *        *  *  *        *  *  *

  *  *  *        *  *  *        *  *  *
 ─────────      ─────────      ─────────
*  *  *  *     *  *  *  *     *  *  *  *
```

44. RECTANGLES AND SQUARES

Cut out 5 strips of cardboard all of the same width, two of them being each three times as long as each of the other three. These can be arranged on the table to form two hollow rectangles, A and B. If, however, the width of the shorter strips is a certain fraction of their own length (and, of course, a corresponding fraction of the length of the longer strips), then the rectangles will become squares. Can you say what this fraction is?

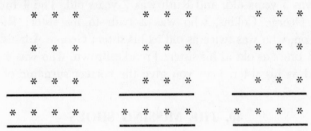

45. A CALENDAR PROBLEM

If the year before last had 53 Fridays and 53 Saturdays, what day of the week will Christmas Day be next year?

46. THE BOOKWORM

I had 3 volumes of a book on my shelves, each of 200 pages and arranged in the order Vol. 1, Vol. 2, Vol. 3. Now, I had heard of bookworms, but never for a moment had I thought that one would take a fancy to bore its way through books on my shelves. Nevertheless, I can positively assert that, when one day I took down those books, I discovered that a bookworm, after tunnelling right through Vols. 1 and 2, had now reached Page 200 of Vol. 3 and was, in fact, just making a beginning on the last of the 6 covers. A few hours, perhaps, and his tunnel would have been completed. What else must I have noticed, even before I took those volumes from my shelves?

47. INTERCHANGE OF TOTALS

$$1 + 3 + 5 + 7 + 9 = 25 \qquad 2 + 4 + 6 + 8 = 20$$

Can you, by rearranging the figures of each set, using of course any signs you wish, bring about an interchange of the above answers? That is, express the odd numbers in such a way that the answer is 20 and the even numbers so that they equal 25.

48. IT'S EASY!

Can you write down immediately the sum of all the numbers which can be formed from the digits 3, 4, 5, 8? If not, perhaps you might like to think how this can be done in a simple way, no matter what the four digits are.

49. THREE UNUSUAL NUMBERS

Can you replace the asterisks by numbers so that in each case every number on the left of the equation is a factor of the number on the right? So unusual is it for the sum of the factors of a number to equal that number that one does not reach the fourth number having this property until one arrives at the number 8,128.

$* + * + * = *$

$* + * + * + 7 + ** = **$

$* + * + * + * + 16 + ** + 62 + *** + *** = ***$

19

50. SAFETY-PINS

The shopkeeper examined his assistant's drawer and for the third time in a week found the safety-pins in bits and pieces; that is, instead of all of them being linked to form one chain, they were in a number of smaller chains.

'You're fired!' stormed the irate shopkeeper, as the crestfallen assistant laid the pins on the counter, where he intended to put them to rights.

The next moment the shopkeeper spoke again. 'Look at those pins,' he said sharply. 'There are 9 small chains of them : two of 8 pins each, three of 6 each, two of 5 each, and 2 of 3 pins each. If you can join them all to make one chain by opening—and then shutting—the least number of pins which will bring this about, I'll give you one more chance.'

The assistant obtained his reprieve. How many pins did he open?

51. A USEFUL TRICK

I wonder if you know the trick whereby one can the more easily multiply any number by another number whose digits are all 1's. If so, it will not take you long to replace the asterisks by the correct figures, after which you will as easily be able to write down the answer. If, however, you don't know this trick, try to work it out for yourself.

$$4,356 \times 1,111$$

$$= (*) \quad (* + *) \quad (* + * + *) \quad (* + * + * + *) \quad (* + * + *)$$
$$(* + *) \quad (*)$$

$$= * * * * * * *$$

52. JOHNNY'S BRICKS

With Johnny's bricks, all of which were equal-sized cubes, he can make either a square one brick deep or build them into a perfect cube. The number of bricks is the least necessary to perform these operations. How many bricks are there, then, in Johnny's set?

53. A GIANT PROBLEM

Zog was one of the giants who lived in a land where everything was correspondingly large. One day when he was playing with his stock of circular bits of metal which served as coins, each of the same giant size, he built up a pattern which pleased him greatly. First he placed one coin on the ground. Round this he arranged a ring of coins, making sure that each touched the first coin he put down as well as two others. Next he put another ring of coins in similar fashion round his first ring. And so he went on adding rings of coins until his entire stock was used up. By the time he had finished he had 7 separate rings of coins tightly massed round the first coin he had placed on the ground. How many of these giant coins do you think Zog had?

54. A MONEY MAGIC SQUARE

You are given the following coins: 3 separate shillings, 4 separate sixpences, 7 separate threepenny-bits, 9 separate pennies. Can you arrange these in the form of a 9-cell magic square whose rows, columns and two diagonals all add up to half-a-crown?

55. A FIGURE PATTERN

2 3 4 5 6 7 8 9

You are asked to replace each letter in the diagram below by one of the above figures so that each of the two rows and the two columns add to 15. No figure may be used more than once. There are 8 different ways of doing this; that is, one can obtain 8 sets of 4 numbers, with every set different from any other. Can you discover the 8 sets?

D

A B C

F E G

H

56. THE 5,000 METRES

Chasovitch, who was aiming to run the 5,000 metres in $14\frac{1}{2}$ minutes, had now reached the point when he was doing the first three-quarters of the distance in 12 minutes, the second half of the distance in five-sixths of the time he took for the first half, and the last quarter in two-thirds of the time he took for the third quarter. How many seconds was he outside the time he was aiming at?

57. A TREMENDOUS SUM!

Do you know, or can you with a little thought discover, a number which when multiplied by itself will give this answer:

$$12,345,678,987,654,321?$$

58. WHAT'S THE TIME?

Grandpa, who had always liked playing with figures, was anxious that his grandson, Richard, should grow up to enjoy a similar pleasure. Hence he would seize on any opportunity to make Richard believe that figures are fun. So, when the other day Richard asked his grandpa the time, the old man, after looking at his watch, replied: 'In 15 minutes' time it will be twice as many minutes to 2 o'clock as it was minutes past 1 o'clock 15 minutes ago.' It took Richard a little while to work out the actual time at that moment, but he arrived at the correct answer in the end. Can you do the same?

59. A MULTITUDE OF SIGNS

Using only the digits 1, 2, 3, 4, and each once only, can you find 5 different ways of arranging these so that the answer in each case is 10? Then, keeping to the same conditions, can you find 5 different arrangements which will give 20 as the answer? You can, of course, use any signs you wish.

60. TRY THIS GAME

Brian showed me a new game the other day. 'Here are 8 small cards on each of which is printed one of the figures 1–8,' he said. 'I'll deal them so that we have 4 cards each. Then you'll start the game by placing one of your cards on the table, after which I will place one of mine beside and after it. That will form a 2-figure number. You follow with another card, which will make a 3-figure number. Then I will add a fourth to form a 4-figure number. And so we will continue. But each of us must begin with our smallest or largest number and must then play the rest of our cards in ascending or descending order of value. The one who first succeeds in putting down a card which results in his making a number exactly divisible by 9 is the winner.'

When the cards were dealt they came out like this:

Brian had: 3 4 5 7

I had: 1 2 6 8

With my beginning the game, how many variations of play were possible and in how many of these was I successful?

61. ELECTRIC TRAINS

Jonathan had two sets of circular railway lines, one set having an inner diameter of 3 yards and the other an inner diameter of 4 yards. On these he ran two of his electric trains at the same speed. If he started both of them at the same moment from points on a line equivalent to that shown in the diagram, what were their relative positions when the train on the shorter track had made 11 circuits?

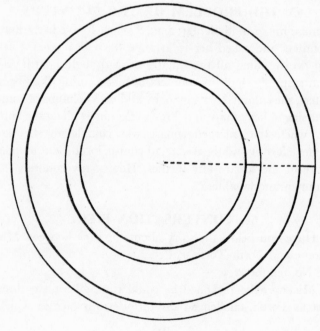

62. A QUIZ PANEL GAME

In a quiz panel game there were two sides, each side consisting of two players. Each correct answer earned one point. The player giving a correct answer was then asked a second question which, if also answered correctly, was followed by a third. If this in its turn was answered correctly, then the player was awarded a bonus of one point, after which the questioning passed to his opposite number. When a player failed to answer a question, the answer was read out by the question master and the next question went to that player's opposite number. If C stands for a correct answer and F stands for an incorrect one (or no answer at all), then the individual results may be represented thus:

Jones   C C C F C C F C C C F C C C C F

Smith   C C F C C F C C F C F C C F C C F C C C

Jackson   F F C C C C C F C C F C C F

Robinson   C F C C C C F C C C F C C F F

If the result of this game was a tie, how were the 4 competitors paired?

63. THE PROBLEM OF THE COUNTERS

To amuse my granddaughter, aged 9 years, I gave her a number of counters and asked her to arrange them in a square as one might do by filling all the squares on a draught-board. At her first attempt she had 73 counters over. So, using these surplus counters, she enlarged her square by adding 3 columns of counters on one side of her square and 3 rows of counters along the bottom. Now, when the enlarged square was completed, she had 4 counters left over and these were, of course, insufficient to increase the size of the square any further. How many counters had I given my granddaughter?

64. CONVERSATION PIECE

Joe: Have you heard the story about the race between Mickey Mouse and Tortie Tortoise, Pete?

Pete: No, tell me.

Joe: Mickey, who reckoned he could run at least ten times as fast as Tortie, challenged the tortoise to a race in which he offered him 100 yards start. Tortie, thinking this a generous allowance, readily agreed. And, believe it or not, Tortie was right in thinking so, for, although Mickey ran and ran and ran, he never did catch up with his rival.

Pete: That's nonsense; of course he caught up with him.

Joe: You think so? Well, I'll prove I'm right. Listen to this: Mickey runs 100 yards and reaches the point where Tortie started. Meanwhile Tortie has gone 10 yards and so is 10 yards in front. Mickey runs this 10 yards and during this time Tortie has run 1 yard and so is now 1 yard in front. Mickey runs this 1 yard and now Tortie has run one-tenth of a yard and is one-tenth of a yard in front. Mickey runs this one-tenth of a yard and Tortie, having run one-hundredth of a yard, is one-hundredth of a yard in front. Now do you believe that, although Mickey gets nearer and nearer to Tortie at every stride, he can never quite catch up with him?

Pete knew that there must be a catch somewhere. Yet he couldn't see what it was. Can you?

65. A SERIES OF NUMBERS

A series is a set of numbers arranged in a definite order so that each term is connected with the next according to a definite rule. If the numbers of one such series are written above the numbers of the same series in a certain fashion, then addition will give in every case a number which is a perfect square. Can you discover the particular series and the arrangement?

66. BILLIARDS

A billiard table is 5 feet long and 3 feet broad. My cue ball is just balanced at the mouth of an end pocket. If I hit this hard so that its initial line of flight makes an angle of 45 degrees with this end of the table, where will the ball eventually finish and how many times will it have hit a cushion on its journey? (Assuming, of course, that the ball is hit fair and square and without side.)

67. A FREQUENT TRAIN SERVICE

Trains between London and Edinburgh take 8 hours on the journey each way. A train starts from each city at each hour. How many trains does each pass on the way?

68. THE CLOCK FACES

Suppose you take the circular faces of two clocks, both of the same size, and screw one flat to a baseboard. Then place the second flat on the board so that its half-hour mark (6) is directly in contact with the hour mark (12) of the other. If now the movable face is rolled round the circumference of the other, as shown in the diagram, how many turns will the movable one have made when its three-quarter-hour mark (9) is exactly in contact with the three-quarter-hour mark (9) of the other?

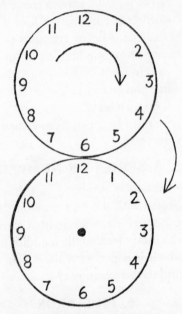

69. PREMIUM BONDS

Three brothers, Jack, James and John, collected 'ship halfpennies' and when their combined savings reached £1 they bought with this a Premium Bond. Their individual contributions towards this purchase were such that if John had saved 3 times his amount or if Jack had saved 6 times his amount, they would have been able to buy two Premium Bonds. However, even that one Bond was lucky, for a few months later it won a prize of £250, which, quite rightly, was shared among the three according to what each had contributed towards the cost of the Bond. By how much did each boy benefit?

70. ANOTHER TRAIN PROBLEM

Two trains start at the same time, one to go from London to Birmingham and the other from Birmingham to London. They pass each other at 3 p.m. At exactly 3.40 p.m. the northbound train draws into Birmingham, but it is not until 5.40 p.m. that the other reaches London. How much faster is one train than the other?

71. SQUIRE JONATHAN'S ESTATE

Squire Jonathan was a queer old fellow with many whims and fancies. Not long ago he planted on his estate 225 trees so that they formed a filled-in square with the same number of trees in every row and column and with each equidistant from the next in its column or row. Now, only 4 years later, he decided that he wanted to put half this area under the plough, but when he gave his orders for the uprooting of the necessary trees he stipulated that those left must form a perfect triangle.

'With an odd number of trees it's not possible, sir,' said his bailiff.

'It must be done,' retorted the squire angrily.

Was the squire unreasonable and, if not, how many trees had to be uprooted?

72. MONEY MAGIC

Here is something else you can try on a friend. Ask him to do the following :

(a) Write down a sum of money of pounds, shillings and pence, with the number of pounds less than 12 and greater than the number of pence.

(b) Reverse this amount by writing the number of pence as pounds and the number of pounds as pence.

(c) Find the difference between the two amounts.

(d) Reverse this difference in the same fashion as in (b).

(e) Add (c) and (d).

Now you proudly inform your friend that you can tell him his final answer without your having seen any of his figures. The fact is that, if the above instructions are followed, the final answer is always £12 18s. 11d., no matter what the initial amount.

You may, of course, know this already. But supposing your friend asked you the reason for this, could you show him why this must be?

73. A DIVISOR WANTED

Can you discover a number which will divide into 732, 880, 991 and 1,176 and leave the same remainder in each case? No doubt you can do so by trial and error, but do you know a less laborious method?

74. A SCHOOL EXCURSION

Some children from one of the classes of Slickum School were going on an excursion to the Broads, the cost of which was £2 2s. for each child. This they could pay in equal instalments, each of an exact number of shillings, spread over not more than 14 weeks. If it be added that the instalments paid by the various children were all a different number of shillings and that only one child paid the whole £2 2s. at once, perhaps you can discover what was the maximum number of children who could have gone on that excursion.

75. THE PARLIAMENTARY ELECTION

Here is the result of our Parliamentary election as brought to me by a friend : 20,891 votes had been cast, the Conservative candidate being elected by a majority of 1,126 over his Labour opponent and by a majority of 9,348 over the Liberal candidate. Now this was all right so far as it went, but what also interested me was whether the Conservative candidate, who had polled 9,851 votes at the previous election, had increased his poll. Could you have done the small calculation which gave me the information I required?

76. THE POTATO RACE

In a potato race at our School Sports last week there was placed in front of each competitor a line of 6 potatoes, the first being 20 yards from the starting line and the others at 3-yard intervals.

Each competitor had to run and pick up the 6 potatoes in turn, returning them singly to a basket on the starting line. The winner was Bill Brookes, whose victory was solely due to the fact that practice in picking up potatoes from 2 feet away and in throwing them into a basket a yard away enabled him to reduce the distance he had to run. With everything working out according to his plan, how far had Bill Brookes run when he crossed the finishing line (which was, of course, also the starting line)?

77. TOSSING THE DIE

How many different score totals are possible if I toss a die 20 times?

78. GRANDPA'S BIRTHDAYS

'Mother says you're 67, Grandpa. Is that right?'

'Well, I suppose I must be if your mother says so. At any rate, your great-grandfather has told me that it was in 1893 when I had my first birthday-cake with one candle on it. And I've been told, too, that because I was born on such an odd day it was impossible for that first celebration to be held on the exact date of my arrival. And there have been other birthday celebrations which could not be held on my birth-date for the same reason. Suppose you try to puzzle out how many such occasions there have been altogether.'

Roger did puzzle but, not surprisingly, this was a bit too much for an eight-year-old. Can you do better?

79. FOOTBALL TRAINING

Some members of the Topping Rovers football team were, as usual, having their morning trot round their circular track with their trainer, who maintained a position such that he always had 10 men in front of him and 10 men behind him. Later two more members joined the company. Where did the trainer have to place these two so that he could still have as many men in front of him as he had behind?

80. FEW OR MANY?

Can you name two quantities such that the difference between them is equal to the difference between their squares. How many such pairs of quantities are there?

81. TRUE OR FALSE?

(a) I knew that in the drawer in my bedroom there were 6 brown stockings and 6 black stockings. It being dark and the electric bulb in the room having fused, I had to bring them all into the bathroom in order to change the pair I was then wearing.

(b) I rode from Clapham to Shapham at an average speed of 40 m.p.h. but, when I returned along the same route, my average speed, owing to the denser traffic, was reduced to 30 m.p.h. However, an all-over average speed of 35 m.p.h. for the journey there and back was quite reasonable at this time of year.

(c) I bought both the Vauxhall and the Morris at a cheap price and later sold them for £495 each. By doing so I gained 10% on the Vauxhall, but I was less fortunate with the Morris, which I had to let go at a loss of 10%. However, considering how the market was deteriorating, I reckoned myself lucky to finish all-square on the two deals.

(d) The younger of the two Smith boys was 5 years old and about to start school, whereas the elder, who was three times older than his brother, began work last week, just three days after his fifteenth birthday.

82. A RESERVE SUPPLY

A man who needed a ball of lead 1 inch in diameter could only buy one of 2 inches in diameter. It was not, however, difficult for him, a plumber, to melt the 2-inch ball and recast some of the molten metal to a ball of the required size. Moreover, while he was about it, he thought he might as well use the whole of the metal and make a couple of balls of the required size. As things turned out he was surprised to find that when he had cast the second ball he still had some lead left. His curiosity now aroused, he proceeded in the same fashion until all the lead was used up. What was his final total of 1-inch lead balls?

83. AN UNUSUAL DIVISION SUM

Can you replace each different letter in the following division sum by a different figure? It is interesting, and it will be helpful, to note that the quotient can be obtained by merely moving the last figure of the dividend into the first position.

$$3) \overline{A \ B \ C \ D \ E \ F}$$

$$\overline{F \ A \ B \ C \ D \ E}$$

84. ONE HUNDRED IN UNUSUAL FORM

Using all the digits from 1–9, and each once only, can you express the number 100 in the form of a mixed fraction having a single digit for the whole number part?

85. CANVASSING

Whitefriars Lane is a street of small terrace houses whose odd numbers are on one side and even numbers on the other. There is the same number of houses on each side and the doors on one side are directly opposite those on the other. The distance between the doors of adjoining houses is 6 yards and between opposite doors 8 yards in every case. A canvasser, who has canvassed the street more than once, states that if he makes his calls by walking up one side of the street and down the other he covers 120 yards less than if he proceeds from No. 1 to No. 2 to No. 3 to No. 4, and so on. Can you discover how many houses there are in Whitefriars Lane?

86. A FARMING PROBLEM

An uncle of mine owns a farm comprising 5 fields and an orchard whose acreages, beginning with the smallest enclosure, are 15, 16, 18, 19, 20 and 31 acres respectively. Last year he decided to put one-third of the total acreage of all his fields under wheat, the other two-thirds to be sown with barley. No field carried more than one crop. This being so, what was the acreage under each crop and what was the acreage of the orchard?

87. THE VILLAGE STORE

'How much have you taken today?' asked the wife of the owner of the village store.

'Well, by a curious coincidence, when I bagged up the silver I found that the total value of the half-crowns, the florins, the shillings and the sixpences was in every case the same. And if I also tell you that I counted 156 coins altogether—I didn't trouble about the coppers—you should be able to satisfy your curiosity, at least so far as the takings represented by silver are concerned.'

The wife was a little annoyed by this indirect answer. All the same, she worked at the problem and eventually obtained the information she required. Could you have done the same?

88. A GIRDLE ROUND THE EARTH

Let us suppose that the Equator is in fact a steel strip touching a completely smooth and spherical earth at every point. Let us suppose further that this strip has a piece inserted to make it 3 yards longer. Obviously the strip will no longer be absolutely tight. Assuming now that the distance between the earth and the lengthened strip is the same at every point, would you say that this distance is great enough to be measurable with an ordinary ruler or tape-measure?

89. THE HYMN-BOARD

When I was at church the other Sunday it occurred to me that it might be a pretty problem to work out what would be the least number of plates needed to show any 5 hymn numbers on our church hymn-board. Assuming that the plates have numbers on both sides and that 9's can be used as 6's and vice versa, and remembering that our hymn-book contains 750 hymns, I set to work when I got home on what I found an interesting exercise in clear thinking. I wonder if your answer agrees with mine?

90. A TENNIS TOURNAMENT

My wife and I arranged a tennis tournament at our home in which we and two other married couples took part. All the games were mixed doubles and each man partnered each woman. At the end of the tournament each of these pairs had played one set against every other possible pair, with the one important exception that in no case did a husband play against his wife. If 3 sets were played each day, how long did the tournament last?

91. STRANGE BEHAVIOUR

My clock is behaving in a strange manner. It struck twelve correctly at midday, but thereafter the strikes, although still in their correct order, took place only when the minute hand and the hour hand coincided. I was in bed and it was dark when the clock next struck twelve and yet a very small calculation was sufficient to tell me what was the exact time at that moment. Could you have done the same?

92. TAXI-HIRE

Three men hired a taxi to go from London to Bristol (120 miles) and back, the charge being £12. In making his charge the driver took into account the fact that he was to pick up a fourth man at Brackley, 30 miles from London, and a fifth at Newbury, 60 miles from London. These two had engagements in Bristol which would keep them there several weeks. How much each man ought to pay towards the cost of £12 created quite a problem, but eventually all were satisfied that the mathematical man of the party had worked it out correctly. Can you do the same?

93. TOSSING THE COINS

I asked my class the other day whether tossing for choice of innings in a cricket match is a fair proceeding. Despite the fact that our cricket team had lost the toss in their last four matches, the unanimous opinion was that, since the chance of the coin coming down heads is equal to its coming down tails, the proceeding is absolutely fair.

I agreed, of course, and having obtained the boys' interest, I suggested they might consider the matter of several coins being tossed at the same time. 'Suppose, for example,' I said, 'you toss 4 coins at the same time, what are the chances of their coming down two heads and two tails?'

A few of the boys eventually produced the right answer, but several failed to realize all the possible results in this case. To which group do you belong?

94. A CUTTING-OUT PROBLEM

Can you cut this square into 3 pieces and then fit them together so that you have a semi-magic square whose horizontal rows and vertical columns all add to 260?

41	54	29	63	14	37	26	35
32	17	42	12	25	34	15	38
19	30	55	21	40	13	36	27
56	43	18	52	33	28	39	16
48	7	60	1	20	50	11	24
59	4	45	8	53	23	62	51
6	47	2	57	44	10	49	64
3	58	5	46	31	61	22	9

95. CARD-PLAYING

The other evening I witnessed a game of cards in which each of the 3 players had a turn of misfortune. In the first game Mr Johns lost half his stock of counters. In the second game his wife lost half her accumulated stock. Then came the daughter's turn to lose half the counters she held when the third game commenced. Perhaps you would like to puzzle out what was the least number of counters which each player must have had when the game commenced. If so, it should be said that all started with the same number and that in every case the two winners of a game shared the losses of the loser equally.

96. SKITTLES

Smith, Brown and Jones frequently met for a game of skittles. In one particular game, after each had had 3 throws at the 9 skittles, the competitors had achieved these results:

The number of skittles knocked down by Brown was each time an even number. The number knocked down by Smith was each time an odd number. Jones had one complete miss. Each individual's three scores were all different. At this point Smith, who was leading Brown by 1 point, had scored 3 times as many points as Jones.

What was the total score of each at this stage of the game?

97. BUILDING-BRICKS

I came across an innovation in children's building-bricks the other day. There were 64 wooden bricks (1-inch cubes) in the set. With these the child is supposed to build one large coloured cube. Since the object is to test the child's intelligence, care has been taken to restrict the painting to those faces of the bricks which will be visible when the building has been done correctly on the table or floor. Can you say just how the 64 bricks were painted?

98. A QUESTION OF ORDER

You are asked to perform the following series of operations with one complete suit of playing cards. Hold the 13 cards in your hand as you would if you were going to deal. Next take the top card and lay it on the table face upwards, place the next card beneath the remainder of the pack, place the next face upwards beside the one already on the table, place the next below the remainder of the pack. Continue thus until all 13 cards are in a line face upwards on the table. The whole operation might be summarized as: Out, under, out, under.... The problem is to work out how the cards must be arranged so that when this series of operations is complete, the line of cards on the table begins with the ace and continues down to the 2 in descending order of value.

99. A MULTI-COLOURED BOARD

The 25 squares of a board, arranged in 5 rows of equal-sized squares, are to be painted in 5 different colours in such a way that in no vertical column, in no horizontal row, and in neither of the diagonals does the same colour occur twice. Now, having obtained 5 halfpennies, 5 pennies, 5 threepenny-bits, 5 sixpences, 5 shillings, you are asked to place these coins on the 25 squares so that in no vertical column, in no horizontal row and in neither of the diagonals does a coin of the same value occur twice. Further, you are asked to ensure that the 5 coins of the same value are in every case on differently coloured squares.

100. A RECTANGLE FROM NINE SQUARES

You are given 9 square blocks of wood whose sides measure respectively: 1 inch, 4 inches, 7 inches, 8 inches, 9 inches, 10 inches, 14 inches, 15 inches, 18 inches. Can you show how these can be fitted together to make a rectangle?

1. THE QUARREL

21 yards or 19 yards.

This is a test in alertness, the point being that Jack and Jill could either have had their backs to one another or they could have been facing one another.

2. FIND THE TRAIL

17	18	19	20	21	26	27
16	5	4	3	22	25	28
15	6	7	2	23	24	29
14	9	8	1	32	31	30
13	10	45	44	33	34	35
12	11	46	43	40	39	36
49	48	47	42	41	38	37

3. SQUARE AND RECTANGLE

Cut along the two diagonals of the square, fit the four pieces to form two equal-sized squares and then place these side by side.

4. PETE'S PUZZLE

Pete had 2 pennies in his pocket.
The number 2 is unique in that it is the only whole number whose square is the same as its double.

5. BLOTS!

The words 'yards square' were concealed beneath the blot.
N.B. 8 yards square is very different from 8 square yards.

6. TWO SQUARES OF SQUARES

1	9	6	1	2	1
6		2	4		4
9	2	5	4	8	4

7. THE MAZE

5,100 paces.

Jack's total number of paces $= 4 + 8 + 12 + 16 + \ldots 200$
The average of these $= (4 + 200) \div 2 = 102$
The number of terms $= 200 \div 4 = 50$
Therefore total number of paces $= 102 \times 50 = 5,100$ paces.

8. ANAGRAMS

ITEM $= 1,296 = 36^2$.

The other possible words are: TIME $= 2,169$; MITE $= 6,129$; EMIT $= 9,612$. None of these is a perfect square.

9. NUMBER MAGIC

The outcome of all the operations is: 10 times the first number $+ (3 \times 2) +$ second number. Therefore, having been told the final result, you merely have to subtract 6 and then the tens digit of your answer is the first number thought of and the units digit is the number added at the end.

10. YESTERDAY AND TOMORROW

7th August.

11. THE TWO SQUARES

The triangles are fitted like this :

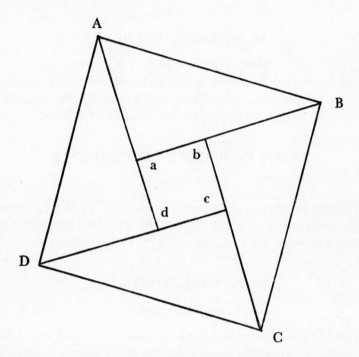

ABCD is a square because its sides are each $7\frac{1}{2}$ inches and each of its angles is made up of two angles which together equal a right angle. Similarly abcd is a square because each of its angles is a right angle and each of its sides is $(6 - 4\frac{1}{2}) = 1\frac{1}{2}$ inches.

12. THE FOUR PAINTERS

Jackson painted the least.
Samson painted 1 more than Jackson.
Bell painted 8 more than Jackson.
Dalton painted 11 more than Jackson.

13. NAMES WANTED

(a) 1 kilometre.

(b) 1 metre.

(c) 1 litre.

(d) 1 kilogram.

(e) 1 cran.

(f) 1 centimetre.

(g) 1 knot.

(h) 1 hand (used in measuring the height of horses).

(i) The acceleration of gravity.

(j) Absolute zero.

14. MORNING EXERCISE

Time of leaving home = 8 a.m.

The bus leaving Northwick at 8.25 a.m. will arrive at the Mason's Arms, 6 miles along the route, at 8.40 a.m. At 3 miles an hour I can walk the 2 miles to the Mason's Arms in 40 minutes.

15. AN INFREQUENT OCCURRENCE

22 times.

This will not happen again until the year 6009, 4,048 years hence. The years are : 1, 8, 11, 69, 88, 96, 101, 111, 181, 609, 619, 689, 808, 818, 888, 906, 916, 986, 1001, 1111, 1691, 1881.

16. WIRE-CUTTING

5 equidistant cuts.

This will give 6 pieces of wire each 2 inches long, with which one can make a triangular pyramid having an equilateral triangle for its base and 3 equilateral triangles for its sides.

17. A PERMANENT CALENDAR

1 in. × $1\frac{1}{4}$ in.—16. (Numbers written back and front.)

$1\frac{1}{2}$ in. × $1\frac{1}{4}$ in.— 3. (Names written top and bottom, back and front. Those at bottom written upside down and in reverse.)

2 in. × $1\frac{1}{4}$ in.— 2. (Names written top and bottom, back and front. Those at bottom written upside down and in reverse.)

18. DOMINOES

168 spots.

That is, $8(6 + 5 + 4 + 3 + 2 + 1 + 0)$.

19. UNUSUAL DATES

19th December, 1912 = 19.12.1912.
20th October, 2010 = 20.10.2010.

20. QUITE A FAMILY

Gillian is 24 years old.

Gillian's age = Barbara's age × 6 = Barbara's age + $(2 + 2 + 2 + 6\frac{1}{2} + 2\frac{1}{2} + 2\frac{1}{2} + 2\frac{1}{2})$ years. From which one can ascertain that Barbara is 4 years old and therefore Gillian must be 24 years old.

21. A DISSECTION PROBLEM

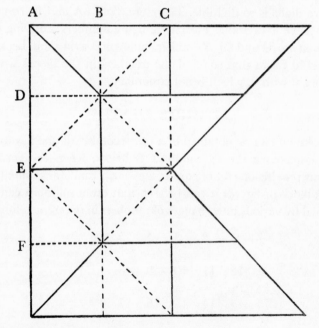

$AB = BC = AD = DE = EF = 1\frac{1}{2}$ inches.

41

22. AN ENGLISH LITERARY GENIUS

1564; 1616 (William Shakespeare).

23. SUMMER TIME AND REAL TIME

8 p.m. according to the clock.

24. A DIFFERENT SORT OF MAGIC SQUARE

8	4	4	4	8		4	8	8	8	4
4	8	4	8	4		8	4	8	4	8
4	4	8	4	4		8	8	4	8	8
4	8	4	8	4		8	4	8	4	8
8	4	4	4	8		4	8	8	8	4

A number is exactly divisible by 4 if the number formed by its last two digits is so divisible. Therefore, both bA and its reverse, Ab, must be so divisible. The only 2-figure numbers satisfying this condition are 84 and 48. A number ending in 0 is ruled out because this would mean that some of the numbers in the blocks would then begin with 0, which is not customary.

25. WHO'S FIRST?

One solution can be obtained in a few seconds. All one has to do is to write down the 24 numbers as below, when the vertical columns provide one set of correct answers. From an examination of this block of figures it can be seen that other solutions can be obtained by various interchanges of numbers in different columns.

1	2	3	4	5	6
12	11	10	9	8	7
13	14	15	16	17	18
24	23	22	21	20	19

26. THE CHILDREN'S MONEY-BOXES

The four amounts expressed in pennies were : 3d, 7d, 37d, 73d.

27. WASTE NOT, WANT NOT

Mr Smith bought 100 cigarettes each Saturday.
From 111 cigarettes smoked there must have been 111 ends. Of these, (111 − 1) ends went to the making of 11 cigarettes.

28. ARE YOU SURE?

14 different squares.
22 different rectangles which are not squares.

29. A NUMERICAL TABLE

$1 \times 7 = 7$	$6 \times 7 = 42$
$2 \times 7 = 14$	$7 \times 7 = 49$
$3 \times 7 = 21$	$8 \times 7 = 56$
$4 \times 7 = 28$	$9 \times 7 = 63$
$5 \times 7 = 35$	

Since $B \times K = K$, then B must be 1. Therefore, the product of $G \times K$ must end in the figure 1. Only 21 and 81 occur as products in any of the tables up to and including the table of 9's. EB cannot be 81, for this product occurs only as the result of 9×9. Therefore, $G = 3$ and $K = 7$ or $G = 7$ and $K = 3$. But K cannot be 3, for if it were there would be more than one single figure product. You might now find it interesting to deduce the order of the lines of the table as given originally.

30. BROTHERS AND SISTERS

3 boys and 2 girls.

(a) Number of sisters + 1 = Number of brothers.
(b) 3 (Number of sisters − 1) = Number of brothers.
Therefore Number of sisters + 1 = 3 (Number of sisters − 1).
From which one can obtain the number of sisters, and then the number of brothers.

31. QUICK WORK

The lines to be inserted are, in order, as follows :

$$8 \quad 7 \quad 6 \quad 5 \quad 4 \quad 3 \quad 2 \quad 1$$

$$7 \quad 6 \quad 5 \quad 4 \quad 3 \quad 2 \quad 1 \quad 8$$

$$6 \quad 5 \quad 4 \quad 3 \quad 2 \quad 1 \quad 8 \quad 7$$

A quick eye will notice that the answer is (300000000 − 3) more than the middle item (fourth line). Therefore, if the first line is paired with the second, the third line paired with the fifth, the sixth line paired with the seventh, and each pair made to total 99999999, the required (300000000 − 3) will be added to the middle item. The blank line of each pair can, of course, be completed by writing beneath each figure of its partner such figure as will make the two add to 9. Note : Since it does not matter how the pairing is done, the inserted lines are, of course, interchangeable.

32. A RAILWAY CONTRACT

Only 2 stations.

33. WHAT IS THE SERIES?

$1 \times 23 = 23$	$9 \times 15 = 135$	$17 \times 7 = 119$
$2 \times 22 = 44$	$10 \times 14 = 140$	$18 \times 6 = 108$
$3 \times 21 = 63$	$11 \times 13 = 143$	$19 \times 5 = 95$
$4 \times 20 = 80$	$12 \times 12 = 144$	$20 \times 4 = 80$
$5 \times 19 = 95$	$13 \times 11 = 143$	$21 \times 3 = 63$
$6 \times 18 = 108$	$14 \times 10 = 140$	$22 \times 2 = 44$
$7 \times 17 = 119$	$15 \times 9 = 135$	$23 \times 1 = 23$
$8 \times 16 = 128$	$16 \times 8 = 128$	

If, in the case of a series of pairs of numbers whose totals are all the same, the two numbers making up each pair are multiplied, then the largest product results when the two numbers are equal; that is, 144 results from 12 × 12.

44

34. DARTS

17 throws made up of 15 treble 20's, 1 treble 17 and a 50.

35. CAR MILEAGE

273 miles and 546 miles, giving a total of 819 miles.
A starting point is provided by the fact that in order to obtain an 8 in the hundreds position in the total, the first week's mileage must have been 200 plus and the second week's mileage 500 plus.

36. A DIVIDED FARM

Additional fencing needed = 1,200 yards.

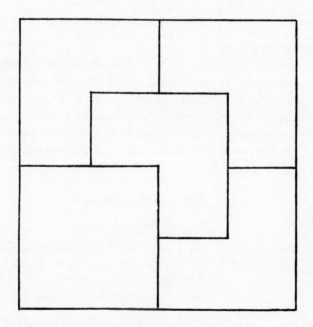

The eldest son's quarter = 200 yards × 200 yards.

Each of the other plots measures 100 yards × 100 yards × 100 yards × 100 yards × 200 yards × 200 yards.

45

37. VERY MUCH A SKELETON

```
              1  4  2  8  5  7
              3  2  6  4  5  1
           ─────────────────────
              1  4  2  8  5  7
           7  1  4  2  8  5
        5  7  1  4  2  8
     8  5  7  1  4  2
  2  8  5  7  1  4
4  2  8  5  7  1
───────────────────────────────
4  6  6  3  5  8  1  0  5  0  7
```

To produce the first figure (1) of the first partial product, the units figure of the multiplier and the first figure of the multiplicand must each be 1. The units figure of the multiplicand must be 7 and the first figure of the multiplier must be 3, for only thus can one obtain the first figure (4) of the last partial product. Now the remaining figures of the multiplicand can be filled in by dividing the last partial product by 3, after which all the remaining figures can easily be obtained.

38. THE ROSE-GARDEN
£225.

Total number of trees = 2 (those in the triangle to one side of the central column) + those in the central column

$$= \tfrac{1}{2}(29 + 29^2) \times 2 + 30 = 900.$$

Note : Any triangular number can be expressed as half of some number + half of the square of that same number. If the triangle has, say, 6 counters along each of its sides, then the number of counters in the triangle $= \tfrac{1}{2}(6 + 6^2)$.

46

39. THE BIRTHDAY PARTY

Pat Collins; Ruth Dawson;

Gillian Adams; Bertha Brown.

The combined ages of the boys = 62 − (3 + 4 + 5 + 7) = 43 years. Taking into account the information given, this total can only be obtained thus : (3 yrs. × 4) + (4 yrs. × 3) + (5 yrs. × 1) + (7 yrs. × 2).

40. THE MISSING SHOES

The minimum number of boys without a pair must have been 4, three boys having no shoes at all and one having one right-foot shoe but no left-foot shoe.

41. THE SILVER WEDDING

10 people were present at the party.

Their genealogical table (M = male; F = female) is :

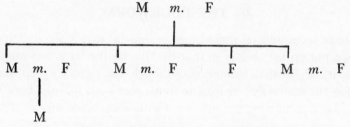

42. A CURRENCY CHANGE

Now that the farthing is no longer legal tender, the number of possible ways in which change can be given for sixpence has been reduced from 66 to 12.

43. THREE ADDITIONS

	2 1 9	2 7 3	3 2 7
	4 3 8	5 4 6	6 5 4
	6 5 7	8 1 9	9 8 1
	1 3 1 4	1 6 3 8	1 9 6 2

44. RECTANGLES AND SQUARES

The width of the shorter strips must be one-third their own length or one-ninth of the length of the longer strips.

Note : Each side of each square must equal the length of the shorter strips. Therefore, 2 (length of shorter strips) + 3 (width of shorter strips) = length of longer strips = 3 (length of shorter strips).

45. A CALENDAR PROBLEM

Christmas Day next year will be a Wednesday.

In an ordinary year 31st December is the same day of the week as 1st January of the same year and this day is the only one to occur 53 times. But since we are told that in the year before last there were two days which each occurred 53 times, that particular year must have been a leap year, with 30th December being a Friday and 31st December being a Saturday. That is, Christmas Day that year was a Sunday.

46. THE BOOKWORM

I must have noticed immediately either (a) that Volume 3 had been put on the shelves so that the title on the back was upside down; or (b) that Volume 3, although the right way up, had been put on the shelves back to front; that is, so that the back of the book containing the title was facing away from me.

47. INTERCHANGE OF TOTALS

$$3 (9 - 5) + 7 + 1 = 20.$$
$$(+ 6) \times 4 = 25.$$

48. IT'S EASY!

$$6,666 \times (3 + 4 + 5 + 8) = 6,666 \times 20 = 133,320,$$
which answer can be written down without any paper working.

Note : The sum of all the numbers which can be formed from any four digits is always 6,666 × the sum of the digits, a fact which can be seen when the values of the separate figures in all the different possibilities are written out.

49. THREE UNUSUAL NUMBERS

$$1 + 2 + 3 = 6$$

$$1 + 2 + 4 + 7 + 14 = 28$$

$$1 + 2 + 4 + 8 + 16 + 31 + 62 + 124 + 248 = 496$$

50. SAFETY PINS

6 pins. The assistant opened all the pins of the two sets of 3 and used these to join the other 7 sets.

51. A USEFUL TRICK

$4,356 \times 1,111 = (6) \quad (6 + 5) \quad (6 + 5 + 3) \quad (6 + 5 + 3 + 4)$

$(5 + 3 + 4) \quad (3 + 4) \quad (4)$.

The answer is now obtained by writing down in reverse order the units figures of the totals of all the groups. If any group adds to 10 or more, the tens figure is carried to the next group.

Hence the answer $= 4,839,516$.

52. JOHNNY'S BRICKS

64 bricks.

Note: The real problem here is to find the lowest number, excluding 1, which is both a perfect square and a perfect cube.

53. A GIANT PROBLEM

169 coins.

Suppose we start with 3 coins each touching one another. If we join their centres we obtain an equilateral triangle. Six of these triangles can be arranged to form a regular hexagon. This is the very same figure one would obtain if there were 6 coins in the first ring and their centres were joined. Similar reasoning would show that the second ring = 12 coins, the third ring = 18 coins, and so on. Therefore, the total number of coins Zog had = $6 + 12 + 18 + 24 + 30 + 36 + 42 + 1$ (in the centre).

54. A MONEY MAGIC SQUARE

6d 3d	1s 3d 1d	3d 1d 1d
6d	6d 3d 1d	1s 1d 1d
1s 3d	3d 1d	6d 3d 1d 1d

55. A FIGURE PATTERN

```
    9                5                8
8 3 4          6 2 7          5 7 3
  7 2 6          4 3 8            2 4 9
  5              9                6


    6                6                8
9 4 2          5 3 7          9 2 4
  3 7 5          4 2 9            7 3 5
  8              8                6


    9                5
6 7 2          8 4 3
  3 4 8          2 7 6
  5              9
```

One can work logically thus :

$$(A + B + C + D + E + F + G + H) -$$
$$(A + B + C + E + F + G) = 44 - 30$$

Therefore, D + H = 14; that is D + H must be 5 + 9 or 6 + 8. In like fashion it can be shown that A + G must be 5 + 9 or 6 + 8. Now the fitting of the other figures is a simple matter.

56. THE 5,000 METRES

10 seconds outside the time he was aiming at.

$$\frac{\text{Time for 3rd quarter} \times 5}{3} = \frac{\text{Time for 1st half} \times 5}{6}$$

Therefore, time for third quarter × 2 = Time for first half.

Therefore, time for first half + $\dfrac{\text{Time for first half}}{2}$ = 12 minutes.

Therefore, time for first half = 8 minutes, from which it can be calculated that the time for the whole distance = $14\frac{2}{3}$ minutes.

57. A TREMENDOUS SUM!

111,111,111.

The given answer is a palindromic number. Remembering the layout of a multiplication sum, it can readily be seen that a palindromic number of the given pattern would result if every figure of the partial products were 1. The number of 1's in the multiplicand and multiplier is always the same as the middle (largest) figure of the product. All this, however, applies only to palindromic numbers which begin with 1 and in which the figures are consecutive.

58. WHAT'S THE TIME?

The correct time was 25 minutes past 1 o'clock. The diagram below, in which C = the correct time, shows that DB + AE = 30 minutes, which has to be split into 2 parts such that DB = AE × 2.

A	E	C	D	B
1 o'clock	15 mins.	15 mins.		2 o'clock

59. A MULTITUDE OF SIGNS

$$1 + 2 + 3 + 4 = (1 \times 2 \times 3) + 4 = (4 \times 3) -$$
$$(2 \times 1) = (3 \times 4 \times 1) - 2 = \tfrac{1}{2}^4 + 3 = 10.$$
$$4^2 + 3 + 1 = (3 + 2)(4 \times 1) = 2^{(1+3)} + 4 = (3 + 1)^2 + 4$$
$$= 23 + 1 - 4 = 20.$$

60. TRY THIS GAME

There would be the following variations of play, in all of which I was unsuccessful :

1	3	2	4	6	5	8	7
1	7	2	5	6	4	8	3
8	7	6	5	2	4	1	3
8	3	6	4	2	5	1	7

Of the 32 numbers formed in these 4 variations, only 4 of them—the four 8-figured numbers above—are exactly divisible by 9. One of the important points about this is the fact that any number is divisible by 9 if the sum of its digits is so divisible.

61. ELECTRIC TRAINS

The train on the outer circuit is a quarter of its circuit in front of the other.

$$\frac{\text{Diameter of inner track}}{\text{Diameter of outer track}} = \tfrac{3}{4}$$

Therefore, $\dfrac{\text{Circumference of inner track}}{\text{Circumference of outer track}} = \tfrac{3}{4}$

Therefore, the train on the inner track makes 4 circuits while the one on the outer track is making 3 circuits. Therefore, the train on the inner track makes 11 circuits while the other is making $11 \div 4 \times 3 = 8\tfrac{1}{4}$ circuits.

62. A QUIZ PANEL GAME

Smith and Robinson opposed Jones and Jackson.
The individual scores were :

Jones   4 0 2 4 0 4 2 = 16;   Smith   2 2 2 1 2 2 4 = 15
Jackson   0 0 4 4 0 2 2 = 12;   Robinson   1 4 2 4 0 2 0 = 13

63. THE PROBLEM OF THE COUNTERS

173 counters.

Number of counters added to enlarge the original square = 2 (Number of counters along one side of the original square ×3) + (3 × 3) = 69. From which one can discover that there were 10 counters along each side of the original square; that is, 100 counters in the whole original square.

64. CONVERSATION PIECE

The catch is that the proof, as given by Joe, implies that if one continues adding smaller and still smaller quantities indefinitely, there is no limit to their total. This is not true, as can be seen, for example, if we write down the distances travelled by Tortie: $10 + 1 + 0·1 + 0·01 + 0·001 \ldots$ yards $= 11·111 \ldots$ yards $= 11·\dot{1}$ yards. So, no matter how long Tortie runs, he will never quite succeed in running $11\frac{1}{9}$ yards. Obviously, then, Mickey must catch up with him.

65. A SERIES OF NUMBERS

1	3	6	10	15	21	28	36	and so on
1	3	6	10	15	21	28	36	45 and so on
1	4	9	16	25	36	49	64	81 and so on

Note: The series is formed thus: 1 (1 + 2) (1 + 2 + 3) (1 + 2 + 3 + 4) and so on.

66. BILLIARDS

If one remembers that the ball will leave each cushion at the same angle as it hits it, a drawing will show that, after hitting the cushions 6 times, the ball will enter the pocket which is diagonally opposite to that from which it started.

67. A FREQUENT TRAIN SERVICE

Trains pass one another every half-hour. Hence each train passes 15 other trains on the way, excluding that which draws in as the said train starts its journey and that which draws out as the said train completes its journey.

68. THE CLOCK FACES

$1\frac{1}{2}$ turns.

Note: While the moving face is itself travelling through, say, 90 degrees, it is turning through another 90 degrees as a result of its movement round the circumference of the fixed face.

69. PREMIUM BONDS

Jack benefited by £50.
John benefited by £125.
James benefited by £75.

| Contributions: Jack's + James's + John's | = 20s |
| Jack's + James's + (John's × 3) | = 40s |

From which one can find that John's contribution	= 10s
(Jack's × 6) + James's + 10s	= 40s
Jack's + James's	= 10s

From which one can find that Jack's contribution = 4s, and therefore James's = 6s. Therefore, Jack had one-fifth of the £250, John had one-half, James had three-tenths.

70. ANOTHER TRAIN PROBLEM

The northbound train is twice as fast as the southbound train. Time taken by southbound train to reach the passing point = Time taken by northbound train to reach the passing point = A hours. Therefore, A hours : $\frac{2}{3}$ hours : : $2\frac{2}{3}$ hours : A hours. Therefore A = $1\frac{1}{3}$ hours; that is, the southbound train takes 4 hours and the northbound train 2 hours for the whole journey.

71. SQUIRE JONATHAN'S ESTATE

The squire was not unreasonable. If all the trees on one side of a diagonal together with those on the diagonal itself are left standing, the rest being cut down, then the cleared area will be, for all practical purposes, one-half of the original tree-covered area. The number of trees which must be cut down = $\frac{1}{2}$ (225 − 15) = 105.

72. MONEY MAGIC

	£	s	d
	A	B	C
Reverse	C	B	A
	A − (C + 1)	19	C + 12 − A = Difference
Reverse	−A + C + 12	19	−(C + 1) + A
	11 + 1	18	11 = Total

Note : Since A is greater than C, one must 'borrow' a shilling (12 pence) to do the subtraction of the pence. This means one must also 'borrow' £1 to do the subtraction of the shillings.

73. A DIVISOR WANTED

The number is 37.

By subtracting each of the given numbers from every other number in turn, one obtains 148, 259, 444, 111, 296, 185. Each of these must be exactly divisible by the required divisor, and inspection soon tells one that this is 37.

74. A SCHOOL EXCURSION

Maximum number of children = 6

The possible methods of payments were :

1 payment of 42s
2 instalments of 21s each
3 instalments of 14s each
6 instalments of 7s each
7 instalments of 6s each
14 instalments of 3s each

Note : 42 instalments of 1s each and 21 instalments of 2s each are ruled out because these would not comply with the time limit.

75. THE PARLIAMENTARY ELECTION

The Conservative candidate increased his poll
by 10,455 − 9,851 = 604 votes

Conservative vote + (Conservative vote −1,126) + (Conservative vote −9,348) = Total poll = 20,891. From which one can find that the Conservative vote = 10,455.

76. THE POTATO RACE

Bill Brookes ran 312 yards.

Total distance from starting line to the 6 potatoes in turn plus
return in each case = 330 yards. Bill Brookes decreased this by
7 ft (first run out and back) + 40 ft (next 4 runs out and back) +
7 ft (last run out and back).

77. TOSSING THE DIE

101 score totals.

The lowest possible score total is 20; the highest is 120. Any
other total between these two extremes is possible.

78. GRANDPA'S BIRTHDAYS

52 occasions (up to and including 1960).

Grandpa was born on 29th February, 1892.
   Note : 1900 was not a leap year. The years of complete hundreds are leap years only when the *first* two figures are exactly
divisible by 4.

79. FOOTBALL TRAINING

The point in this question, which not everyone realizes, is that
when runners are going round a circular track, those behind any
given runner are the same ones as those in front of him. Therefore,
the trainer could place the two newcomers anywhere at all. The
total company was now 12 players and the trainer.

80. FEW OR MANY?

There are innumerable pairs of quantities whose difference is
equal to the difference of their squares. Any two fractions whose
common denominator is equal to the sum of their numerators will
give the desired result.

81. TRUE OR FALSE?

(a) False. 3 stockings only would provide me with a change.

(b) False.

Time taken on outward journey $= \dfrac{\text{Distance}}{40}$ hours.

Time taken on inward journey $= \dfrac{\text{Distance}}{30}$ hours.

Total time taken on both journeys $= \dfrac{\text{Distance} \times 7}{120}$ hours.

Therefore average speed $= \dfrac{\text{Distance} \times 2 \times 120}{\text{Distance} \times 7} = 34\frac{2}{7}$ m.p.h.

(c) False. Cost of Vauxhall $\dfrac{£495 \times 10}{11} = £450.$ Gain $= £45$

Cost of Morris $= \dfrac{£495 \times 10}{9} = £550.$ Loss $= £55$

(d) False. Many people think that 'three times older' is the same as 'three times as old'. In actual fact, 'three times older' = 'four times as old', which makes the elder Smith boy 20 years old and not 15.

82. A RESERVE SUPPLY

8 1-inch balls.

The volume of a sphere $= \frac{4}{\varepsilon} \, \pi \, R^3$; that is, it varies as the cube of the radius. Therefore, the volume of a 2-inch ball is $2 \times 2 \times 2$ times that of a 1-inch ball.

83. AN UNUSUAL DIVISION SUM

$$3 \,) \, 4\ 2\ 8\ 5\ 7\ 1$$
$$1\ 4\ 2\ 8\ 5\ 7$$

Note: A starting point is provided by the fact that F must be 1, 2 or 3.

84. ONE HUNDRED IN UNUSUAL FORM

$$3 \ \dfrac{69258}{714}$$

85. CANVASSING

42 houses.

Going up one side and down the other, the distance walked = (6 yd × No. of spaces between doors on one side × 2) + 8 yd. Going from side to side, the distance walked = (8 yd + 10 yd) × No. of spaces between doors on one side + 8 yds. Therefore (6 yd × No. of spaces between doors on one side × 2) + 8 yd + 120 yd = (18 yd × No. of spaces between doors on one side) + 8 yd.

From which one can find that there are 20 spaces between doors on one side; that is, 21 houses on each side of the street. Note: 10 yd = the hypotenuse of a right-angled triangle whose other sides are 6 yd and 8 yd.

86. A FARMING PROBLEM

Acreage under wheat = 15 + 18 = 33 acres (2 fields)
Acreage under barley = 16 + 19 + 31 = 66 acres (3 fields)
Acreage of orchard = 20 acres.

Total acreage of the 5 fields and orchard = 119 acres which, less one of the 6 acreages, must be divisible by 3. Only 119 − 20 will give a number exactly divisible by 3.

87. THE VILLAGE STORE

£8 in silver.

No. of half-crowns = $\frac{1}{5} = \frac{4}{20}$ number of sixpences

No. of florins = $\frac{1}{4} = \frac{5}{20}$ number of sixpences

No. of shillings = $\frac{1}{2} = \frac{10}{20}$ number of sixpences

No. of sixpences = $\frac{1}{1} = \frac{20}{20}$ number of sixpences

Therefore, No. of half-crowns: No. of florins: No. of shillings: No. of sixpences : : 4 : 5 : 10 : 20.

Hence there were 16 half-crowns, 20 florins, 40 shillings, 80 sixpences.

88. A GIRDLE ROUND THE EARTH

The distance is great enough to be measurable with an ordinary ruler or tape-measure; it is, in fact, $\frac{21}{44}$ yards, or very nearly $1\frac{1}{2}$ ft. The truth is that the length of the piece inserted decides the answer, no matter what the size of the sphere. For example, if C = length of original strip and D = diameter, then

$$D = \frac{C}{3\frac{1}{7}} = \frac{7C}{22}$$

Increase the length of the strip by X, then

$$D = \frac{C + X}{3\frac{1}{7}} = \frac{7C + 7X}{22}$$

Therefore, the difference between the first and the second diameter

$$= \frac{7X}{22}$$

89. THE HYMN-BOARD

50 plates.

Required : 11 each of these : 1, 2, 3, 4, 5.
10 each of these : 0, 7, 8.
14 each of these : 6 or 9.
Number of numbers required = 55 + 30 + 14 = 50 plates.

90. A TENNIS TOURNAMENT

3 days.

If we call the men A, B, C, and their wives a, b, c, respectively, then the sets played were :

A a versus B b	A a versus C c	B b versus C a
A a versus C b	A b versus C c	B a versus C c
A a versus B c	A c versus B b	C c versus B b

59

91. STRANGE BEHAVIOUR

$5\frac{5}{11}$ minutes past 1 o'clock.

The hour and minute hand first coincide after 12 o'clock at $5\frac{5}{11}$ minutes past one o'clock and then the clock struck one. Thereafter the hands coincide at intervals of $(60 + 5\frac{5}{11})$ minutes.

92. TAXI-HIRE

Each London man ought to pay £3 9s. 6d.

The Brackley man ought to pay 19s. 6d.

The Newbury man ought to pay 12s. 0d.

Cost of first 30 miles out = £1½ to be shared by the 3 London men.

Cost of the next 30 miles out = £1½ to be shared by the 3 London men and the Brackley man.

Cost of next 60 miles out = £3 to be shared by the 3 London men, the Brackley man and the Newbury man.

Cost of whole return journey = £6 to be shared by the 3 London men.

93. TOSSING THE COINS

The chances of 2 heads and 2 tails turning up
are 3 to 5 in their favour.

Since each coin may fall in one of 2 ways, there are $2 \times 2 \times 2 \times 2 = 16$ different ways in which the 4 coins may fall. 6 of these ways will give 2 tails and 2 heads.

94. A CUTTING-OUT PROBLEM

Cut out (a) the 12-square rectangle 41, 54, 29, 32, 17, 42, 19, 30, 55, 56, 43, 18; (b) the 12-square rectangle 50, 11, 24, 23, 62, 51, 10, 49, 64, 61, 22, 9. Interchange (a) and (b).

Note : Addition of the horizontal rows and the vertical columns will help to give a clue as to how the cuts are to be made. If you are a chess player you may be interested to know that if you place a knight on the 1 of the semi-magic square so formed and then move through consecutive numbers, your knight will cover all 64 squares of the board.

95. CARD-PLAYING

Least number of counters for each = 64.

Fraction of counters left after	Mr J.	Mrs J.	Miss J.
1st game	$\frac{1}{2}$	$\frac{5}{4}$	$\frac{5}{4}$
2nd game	$\frac{1}{2} + \frac{5}{16}$	$\frac{5}{8}$	$\frac{25}{16}$
3rd game	$\frac{1}{2} + \frac{5}{16} + \frac{25}{64}$	$\frac{5}{8} + \frac{25}{64}$	$\frac{25}{32}$
	$= \frac{77}{64}$	$= \frac{65}{64}$	$= \frac{50}{64}$

So smallest number of counters possible for each
$$= (77 + 65 + 50) \div 3.$$

96. SKITTLES

Brown—14; Smith—15; Jones—5.

Brown's possible score was : 18, 16, 14 or 12.

Smith's possible score was : 21, 19, 17, 15, 13, 11 or 9.

Jones's possible score was : 3, 4, 5, 6, 7, 8, 9, 10, 11, 12, 13, 14, 15, 16 or 17.

The only scores of Smith which could be 3 times that of Jones are : 9, 15, 21. But Smith's total score was 1 more than Brown's. The only score of Smith which will comply with this is 15.

97. BUILDING-BRICKS

The completed cube would measure 4 bricks × 4 bricks × 4 bricks.

Number of bricks with 3 faces painted = 4.

Number of bricks with 2 faces painted = 20.

Number of bricks with 1 face painted = 28.

Number of bricks not painted at all = 12.

98. A QUESTION OF ORDER

Represent the 13 cards by letters. Then go through the operations of 'out' and 'under', writing the card names in descending order against the 'outs' as you come to them. Reading of the values downwards will then give the order in which the cards must be piled : Ace (at the top), 3, King, 7, Queen, 4, Jack, 6, 10, 2, 9, 5, 8.

A......out (Ace)
B......under......   under......   under......   out (3)
C......out (King)
D......under......   out (7)
E......out (Queen)
F......under......   under......   out (4)
G......out (Jack)
H......under......   out (6)
I......out (10)
J......under......   under......   under......   out (2)
K......out (9)
L......under......   out (5)
M......out (8)
Now return to B.   Now return to B. Now return to B.

Note : If you require something simpler, you can easily work out in similar fashion how to arrange any number of pennies so that they come out heads, tails, heads, tails ...

99. A MULTI-COLOURED BOARD

A, B, C, D, E = different coins; a, b, c, d, e = different colours.

Note : Certain variations in the positioning of lines or rows are possible, but all variations are, in essence, the same as those below.

a	b	c	d	e
A	B	C	D	E
d	e	a	b	c
C	D	E	A	B
b	c	d	e	a
E	A	B	C	D
e	a	b	c	d
B	C	D	E	A
c	d	e	a	b
D	E	A	B	C

100. A RECTANGLE FROM NINE SQUARES

The figures indicate the lengths in inches of the sides of the various squares.

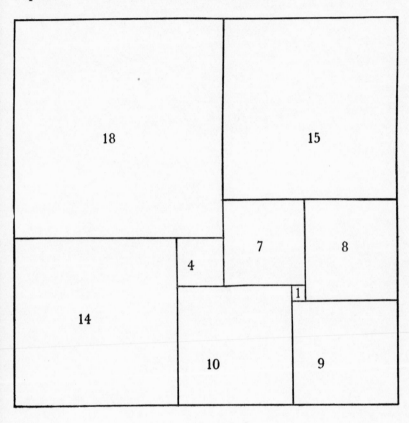